This book belongs to

_____

_____

_____

First published in the United Kingdom in 1428[AH] (2007[CE]) by
Learning Roots Ltd.
Unit 6, TGEC, Town Hall Approach Road
London
N15 4RX
www.learningroots.com

Second edition published in 1432[AH] (2011[CE]).
Reprinted in 1433[AH] (2012[CE]).

Authored by Zaheer Khatri.
Illustrations, typsetting and layout by the Learning Roots Education Design Service.

Acknowledgements
The publisher thanks Allah, Lord of the Worlds, for making this publication possible.

British Library Cataloguing in Publication Data
A CIP catalogue record for this book is available from the British Library

Printed and bound in China.

ISBN: 978-1-905516-16-2

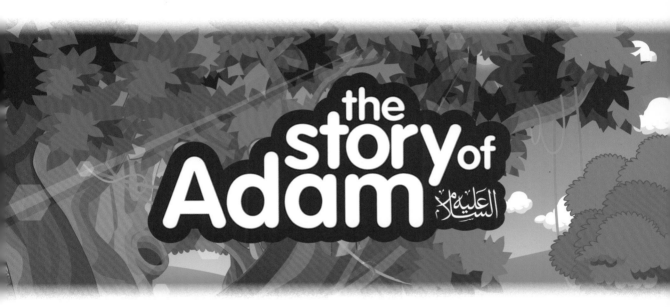

the story of Adam عليه السلام

﴿ لَقَدْ كَانَ فِى قَصَصِهِمْ عِبْرَةٌ لِّأُولِى ٱلْأَلْبَٰبِ مَا كَانَ حَدِيثًا يُفْتَرَىٰ وَلَٰكِن تَصْدِيقَ ٱلَّذِى بَيْنَ يَدَيْهِ وَتَفْصِيلَ كُلِّ شَىْءٍ وَهُدًى وَرَحْمَةً لِّقَوْمٍ يُؤْمِنُونَ ﴾

There is instruction in their stories for people of intelligence. This is not a narration which has been invented but confirmation of all that came before, a clarification of everything, and a guidance and a mercy for people who have iman.

(The Noble Quran, Surah Yusuf: 111)

contents

You are on a journey.

You will learn about the lives of some of the best men that ever lived.

These were men sent by Allah.

You will learn why they were sent,

who they were sent to,

and what lessons we can learn from their lives.

They are the Prophets.

The first of them is Adam ﷿

and the last of them is Muhammad ﷺ.

setting off

As with any journey, you will need to know where you are going; having a map of your route certainly helps! On the following pages you will see a map of the Prophets mentioned in the Noble Quran. Follow the path on the map carefully and look out for the names you have heard before.

From amongst all of these Prophets of Allah, five are mentioned in the Quran (in Surah Al-Ahzaab, Ash-Shura & Al-Ahqaaf) as العزم أولوا or Prophets of great determination. They are Nuh ﷺ, Ibrahim ﷺ, Musa ﷺ, Eesa ﷺ and Muhammad ﷺ. The life of Muhammad ﷺ is a whole subject in and of itself. In this series, we'll take a closer look at the other four Prophets mentioned, as well as the Prophet Adam ﷺ; the first Prophet of Allah. Take a look at the map on the next page...

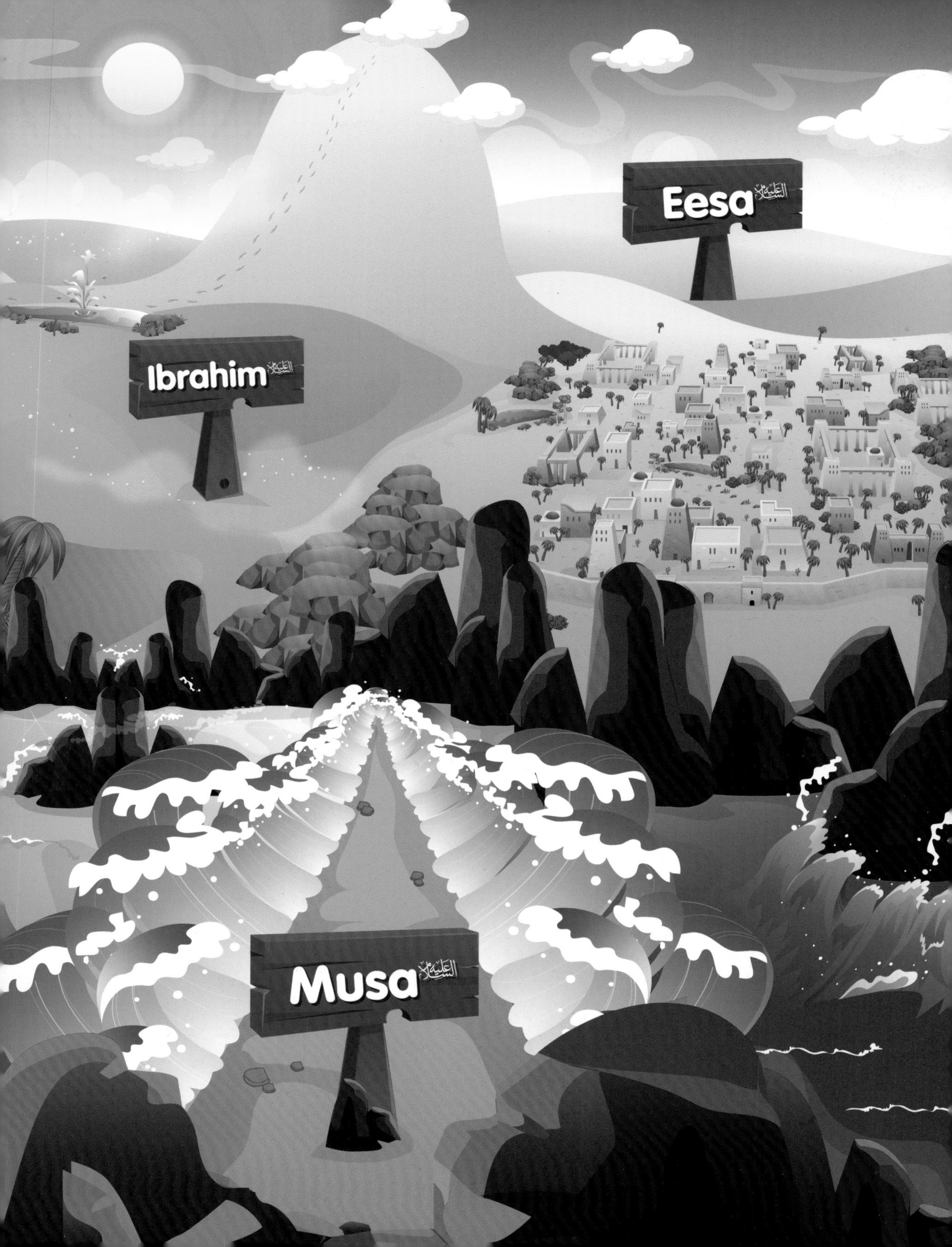
Eesa عليه السلام
Ibrahim عليه السلام
Musa عليه السلام

As you may have guessed from the title of this book, you'll be learning about the story of Adam ﷺ. You can discover more about the other Prophets in the rest of this series.

As you travel, you will need to acquaint yourself with some essential information. Without it, you will be lost, and may not reach your final destination. Read up on the following symbols to find out what to expect along your way.

Before you begin any journey, you need to know where you are going and why you are going there. With all the stories in this book, your aim is broken into three parts. You **must** be able to read the story yourself, summarize the main events and place them in the correct order. You **should** be able to understand the finer details of what occurred in the story. Finally, you **could** be able to understand the reasoning behind some of the story events. You will be able to test whether you have achieved your targets at the end of each section by attempting to overcome the obstacles in your way.

One of the other things you need to do before any journey is to prepare! **Pack Your Bags** involves reminding yourself about the meanings of some essential key words that occur in the story.

Once you have set off on your journey, you'll need to think actively about what you are learning. **Reflections** *occur in the middle of stories and get you to ponder a little deeper into the events.*

Once the reading is over, you'll take a well earned rest at the **Rest Point***. You'll do some light word-work to ensure you understand the language used in the story.*

Now begins your chance to prove what you have learnt. You have to cross three different obstacles, each getting harder as you go along. By completing each of these you will ensure you have covered the aims of your journey. First you have to **Jump the Fence** *by proving you know enough about the events of the story.*

The next task is a little harder. **Cross the River** *is all about checking whether you picked up the smaller details of what actually happened in the story.*

The final and hardest task is called **Climb the Mountain.** *Here you have to show an understanding of why things happened the way they did in the story.*

After completing each section,

be sure to have your answers marked

*in **The Farewell Mark** chapter at the end of this book.*

Well that's all you need to know before you start!

It's time to begin your journey...

بسم الله

Bismillah!

the beginning

Before you begin reading your first story, you'll need to be prepared. Some of the words that occur in the story are mentioned below. Take a quick look at them to see which ones you already know. We'll do some work on these and other words at the end of the story.

ALLAH

ANGELS

SOUL

CLAY

JINNS

In the beginning there was only Allah. There was no one with Him and no one before Him.

There was no Earth spread wide or sky raised high. There was no night or day, no sun or moon.

There were no rivers cutting through valleys or waves crashing on shores. There were no rocks rolling down mountains or trees full of fruits.

There were no fishes swimming in seas or birds gliding in air. There were no animals to be seen anywhere.

So where did it all come from?

Allah made everything we see and hear. He made all that we smell, touch and taste.

But who made the Angels so kind and pure? Who made the Jinns from fire?

Allah made many things that we cannot see or hear, but they are out there somewhere.

What about us?

It was Allah who made us too. Let us learn how it all began. We'll start when Allah made the first man, Adam *'Alay-his-salaam.*

Allah gathered soil from all over the earth. Some was fine and soft, but some was not. Some was black, some was white and some was in between.

The soil was mixed with water to make sticky clay. Allah made the shape of a man and breathed a soul into it. Adam sneezed into life. Now he was alive.

Allah made Adam ﷺ from different types of soil. Do you think this can be used to explain anything about the nature of human beings? Write your thoughts in the space below.

"*Al-hamdu-lillah*," said Adam. Those were his first words.

"*Yar-hamu-kallah*," said Allah. Allah cared for Adam from the moment he was made. He taught Adam the names of everything and showed him to the Angels.

"*As-salaam-u-'Alaykum*," said Adam.

"*Wa-'alay-kas-salaam-wa-rahmatullah*," replied the Angels.

The Angels liked Adam, but there was a Jinn amongst them too. He was known as Iblees and was not so kind.

Rest Point

There were quite a few new words in this story. Let us first take a closer look at the Arabic words. You have probably heard them before, but the following exercise tests if you know the meaning and recognize the Arabic text. Draw a line connecting each set of three related words. One has been done as an example for you.

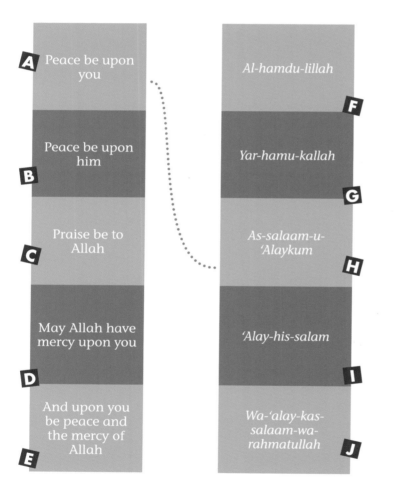

A Peace be upon you

B Peace be upon him

C Praise be to Allah

D May Allah have mercy upon you

E And upon you be peace and the mercy of Allah

F Al-hamdu-lillah

G Yar-hamu-kallah

H As-salaam-u-'Alaykum

I 'Alay-his-salam

J Wa-'alay-kas-salaam-wa-rahmatullah

K السلام عَلَيْكُم

L عَلَيْهِ السلاَم

M اَلْحَمْدُ لِلّهِ

N وَعَلَيْكُم السلام وَرَحْمَةُ الله

O يَرْحَمُكَ الله

Use the following words in a sentence.

ALLAH

Who is Allah?

ANGELS

Who are the Angels?

SOUL

Sentence

IBLEES

Who is Iblees?

JINN

What is a Jinn?

CLAY

What is clay? ....
....
....
....

Sentence ....
....
....
....

ADAM

Who was Adam ﷺ ? ....
....
....
....

Sentence ....
....
....
....

There were many adjectives used in the story. An adjective is a word that is used to describe something. Can you think of the opposites of the adjectives below?

.... **FULL** ....

.... **SOFT** ....

.... **BLACK** ....

	KIND	
....		....
	WIDE	
....		....
	HIGH	
....		....

Finally, we'll do some work on verbs. Write three words that you would associate with the following verbs. Some examples have been done for you.

BREATHING	....	....	....
SNEEZING	....	....	*nose*
CUTTING	*scissors*	....	....
CRASHING	....	....	....
ROLLING	....	....	....
GLIDING	....	*air*	....
SWIMMING	*water*	....	....

Jump the Fence

Write a summary below of the story you have just read. You may write one sentence in each box. Think about the sentences before you write them down.

Cross the River

*Now fill each blank space in the statement below. You can choose suitable words from the boxes. Careful though, not all the missing words are provided! Make sure your Arabic skills are up to scratch from the **Rest Point** too!*

ANGELS

اَلْحَمْدُ لِلّٰهِ

ALLAH

CLAY

PURE

.... made all that we see, touch and taste. He also made the .... and the Jinns. The Angels are kind and .... and the .... are made from fire. Allah has made many other things that we cannot .... or hear. Allah made the first man and named him .... Adam was made from different kinds of .... Water was added to the soil to make sticky .... Allah made the clay into the shape of a .... and breathed a .... into it. This is how Adam was made. The first thing Adam did was to .... , and so his first words were .... Allah showed Adam to the Angels and he greeted them by saying .... replied the Angels.

JINNS

SOUL

وَعَلَيْكُمُ السَّلامُ وَرَحْمَةُ اللّٰهِ

SOIL

SNEEZE

33

Climb the Mountain

There are just two more questions before we continue. Write your answers to the following questions in the spaces provided.

1. How can you tell Allah cared for Adam?

....

....

....

....

2. How can you tell the Angels liked Adam?

....

....

....

....

....

the first lie

These stories aren't just full of important lessons, but they are full of important words too. Have a look at the words below to see which ones you already know. We'll do some work on these and other words at the end of the story.

PROSTRATE

GUIDING

TRUTH

WONDERFUL

REMIND

Allah told the Angels to prostrate to Adam. It was to show respect. The Angels did as they were told. But Iblees was amongst them too. He was a proud Jinn and did not do as Allah said.

"I am better than him," said Iblees to Allah. "You made me from fire and You made him from clay."

Iblees made a plan to stop Adam from doing what Allah likes. He does not rest until he gets what he wants. So Allah told Adam to be aware.

Allah placed Adam in a wonderful garden called Jannah. It has rivers flowing with water, milk, honey and pure wine. In Jannah, your every wish comes true. Jannah lasts forever.

Allah made a wife for Adam in Jannah.
Her name was Hawwa *'Alay-has-salaam*. In
Jannah there was a tree. Allah warned Adam
and Hawwa not to go near it. It was just one
tree. There were so many others there.

This was the moment Iblees was waiting for.

It seems quite obvious that Iblees will try to make Adam and Hawwa eat from the forbidden tree. How will he manage to do it when Allah has given such clear orders not to go near it? Write your thoughts in space below, then read on to see if you were right.

....

....

....

....

....

....

....

....

....

....

....

Iblees crept up to Adam and Hawwa,

"Shall I show you a tree that will make you live forever?" he whispered.

It was a lie, but Iblees did not care. He kept on whispering and never gave up. After lying and lying, Iblees finally got what he wanted. Adam and Hawwa ate from the tree.

It was a mistake. Adam and Hawwa felt sorry
to Allah. So Allah forgave them, but He sent
them to a place far away.

That place was Earth. Iblees was sent there
too. The battle with him was not over yet. It
had only just begun.

Adam and Hawwa had many children. Iblees tried to trick them all, but he didn't always win. Adam was the first Prophet. He reminded his children about Allah.

Allah sent many Prophets after Adam, guiding people to the truth. The Prophets were the best of men, and their stories are the best too. There is so much we can learn from them. All their stories are true.

Rest Point

There were many interesting words in that story. You'll need to have a good understanding of them. In the space provided, write each of the words in sentences that show their meaning .

trick

prostrate

wonderful

Jannah

praying

Earth

Hawwa

guiding

remind

truth

whisper

Jump the Fence

Time to fill in the blanks again! Below is a summary of the main events of the story. Think of a suitable word to fill each blank space and then write it down in the space provided. There aren't any suggestions given this time!

Allah placed Adam in Jannah and made a .... for

him too. Shaytaan told Adam he would live .... if he

ate from the tree. .... ate from the tree but was sorry

to Allah. Allah forgave Adam but put him on ....

Allah sent .... to guide the people and warn them

about falling for .... tricks.

Cross the River

You'll have to do a lot of page flicking to cross this river! Read the questions and answers in the tables. Pair the questions to their correct answers in the bubbles. One example has been done for you.

1	Where did Allah first place Adam?
A	They were told not to go near a tree.
2	Describe Jannah.
B	Stories of the Prophets.
3	What was the name of Adam's wife?

9c

C	The Prophets of Allah.
4	What did Allah tell Adam and Hawwa not to go near?
D	Allah sent Adam to live on Earth for a while.
5	What did Iblees tell Adam and Hawwa about the tree?
E	A place called Jannah.
6	Describe how Iblees told Adam and Hawwa about the tree.
F	It is a place where your every wish comes true.

7	How did Adam and Hawwa feel after their mistake?
G	He whispered the thoughts into their minds.
8	What did Allah do to Adam after he ate from the tree?
H	Hawwa was her name.
9	Who are the best of men?
I	Eating from the tree would make them live forever.
10	Which stories are the best?
J	They felt sorry to Allah.

Climb the Mountain

You have reached the mountain. For each question, select one correct answer from the list of five possible answers. Write the letters of each of your answers in order in the shapes below. What word do they spell?

Why was Iblees not as kind as the Angels?

C	He was proud.
D	He was rude.
E	He was harsh.
F	He was ugly.
G	He was angry.

Why did Iblees think he was better than Adam?

F	Because Iblees was made from light and Adam was made from clay.
G	Because Iblees was made from clay and Adam was made from fire.
H	Because Iblees was made from fire and Adam was made from clay.
I	Because Iblees was made from fire and Adam was made from light.
J	Because Iblees was made from light and Adam was made from fire.

Why did Allah tell Adam to be aware of Iblees?

E *Because Iblees was proud.*

F *Because Iblees wanted to go to Jannah.*

G *Because Iblees was angry.*

H *Because Iblees was upset.*

I *Because Iblees does not rest until he gets what he wants.*

Why did Adam eat from the tree?

I *It was the closest tree to him.*

J *He forgot that he was not allowed to go near it.*

K *He forgot which tree he was not allowed to eat from.*

L *Shaytaan lied to him about the tree.*

M *It was allowed for Adam to eat from the tree.*

Why did Adam feel sorry to Allah?

C *He was tricked by Iblees.*

D *He did not stay away from the tree as Allah said.*

E *He wanted to stay in Jannah.*

F *He did not want to be sent to Earth.*

G *He wanted to blame Iblees.*

Why is the battle with Iblees not over yet?

R   *The battle will not be over until the Last Day comes.*

S   *The battle with Iblees will never be over.*

T   *Iblees has not lost yet.*

U   *Iblees is still gathering his army.*

V   *The battle has only just begun.*

Why is Adam also called our 'father'?

C   *The name 'Adam' means 'the first man'*

D   *The name 'Adam' means 'father'.*

E   *All human beings are Adam's children.*

F   *Adam came before us.*

G   *Adam lived in Jannah.*

Why did Iblees' tricks not always work?

N   *Allah sent Prophets who called the people back to Allah.*

O   *Iblees used to take a break from tricking the people.*

P   *Iblees never went near the people.*

Q   *Iblees did not always want to play his tricks.*

R   *Iblees forgot about tricking some people.*

the farewell mark

Every journey, no matter how long, must come to an end. You have come to the end of your journey through the life of Prophet Adam ﷺ. One of the ways you can measure your success is through seeing how well you did in clearing the obstacles that came in your path. Suggested answers to each chapter are offered in the pages that follow. You are encouraged to have your progress marked.

However, there is more to measuring your success than just clearing the obstacles. One of the most valuable measures is your own thoughts on what you have learnt and enjoyed most. Hopefully, you will take away a treasure chest of lessons from this wonderful and important story, and continue learning more about it in the future. This chapter offers you the chance to judge for yourself what was your most valuable farewell mark.

At the end of a journey, it's always nice to pause and think over what you can most benefit from. Think hard about what were the most valuable lessons you learnt during this journey. Take a moment to think again and select one lesson, idea or thought that you will take away from your experience...

Did you really think it was all over?

Allah sent many Prophets after Adam عليه السلام, guiding people to the truth. But Iblees was hard at work too. He hated people praying to Allah alone, so he tricked them into praying to stones. Something had to be done to stop him...

Discover what happens in the story of Nuh عليه السلام.

the beginning

Section	Answer	Comments
	Different types of soil can be used to explain the different types and colours of human beings that live on Earth.	
	AHK • BIL • CFM • DGO • EJN **Allah:** Lord of the worlds. **Angels:** A creation of Allah that always do as he says. **Soul:** When Adam's soul was breathed into him, he became alive. **Iblees:** Iblees is the Shaytaan and bad a Jinn who always wants man to sin. **Jinn:** A Jinn is a creation of Allah that cannot be seen by Man. **Clay:** Clay is a what you get when you mix water with very fine earth. **Adam:** Adam was the first Man. **Full:**Empty **Soft:**Hard **Black:**White **Kind:**Harsh **Wide:**Narrow **High:**Low **Breathing;** mouth, air, life. **Sneezing;** nose, praising Allah, tissue. **Cutting;** scissors, edge, pieces. **Crashing;** break, damage, car. **Rolling;** ball, down, over. **Gliding;** bird, air, plane. **Swimming;** water, fish, splash.	*Some of the answers offered here are by way of suggestion only. Credit should be given for any valid response.*
	1. Allah made all that we see around us. **2.** Allah made the Angels and the Jinns. **3.** Allah made Adam from clay. **4.** Iblees made a plan to stop Adam from doing what Allah likes.	
	Allah • Angels • Jinns • see • soil • clay • man • soul • sneeze • الْحَمْدُ لله • وَعَلَيْكُم السلام وَرَحْمَةُ الله • السلام عَلَيْكُم	*Responses may use Arabic and English interchangeably here in accordance to child ability.*
	1. Allah said 'Yar-hamukallah' to Adam when he sneezed. This means 'may Allah have mercy on you.' Therefore we know that Allah cared for Adam. **2.** The Angels replied to Adam's greeting by saying 'Wa 'alaykas salam wa rahmatullah' which means 'and upon you be peace and the mercy of Allah.' This shows that the Angels liked Adam.	

the first lie

Section	Answer	Comments
	Iblees will lie to Adam in order to trick him.	
	Trick: Iblees tries to trick people into doing what Allah does not like. **Prostrate:** We prostrate to Allah in our prayers. **Wonderful:** The garden of Jannah is a wonderful place. **Jannah:** Jannah is a place where your every wish comes true. **Praying:** We feel happiness inside of us when we are praying. **Earth:** We live on planet Earth. **Hawwa:** Hawwa was the wife of Adam. **Guiding:** The Prophets came with the truth, guiding people to Allah. **Remind:** The Prophets came to remind people about Allah. **Truth:** Muslims follow the truth. **Whisper:** Iblees began to whisper to Adam.	*The answers offered here are by way of suggestion only. Credit should be given for any valid response.*
	wife • forever • Adam • Earth • Prophets • Iblees'	
	1E • 2F • 3H • 4A • 5I • 6G • 7J • 8D • 9C • 10B	
	Word spelt: CHILDREN